ROCKETS
AROUND THE WORLD

By ERIK BERGAUST

After the success of his *Rockets and Missiles,* published in the fall of 1957, Erik Bergaust began to compile photographs and information for a new book which would include the advances being made by other nations. The result was *Rockets Around the World,* a photographic tour of rockets and missiles being built, tested and operated around the world.

Here is an evaluation of our own missile program, including a brief report on its history. Here, too, is an especially interesting section on the Soviet Union—one of the most extensive reports on the Russian missile program ever published in the United States.

The U. S. and the Soviet Union lead the world in the missile race but other nations, particularly Great Britain, are rapidly developing and expanding their own programs. Since the end of World War II France has advanced steadily. Canada works closely with the United States and Great Britain. Australia, despite financial limitations, is making a major contribution to Western missile progress. Sweden, Switzerland, Japan, Italy—all are presently engaged in intensive missile activity.

Rockets Around the World brings you an up-to-date report by a noted authority on what each of these nations is doing in the race to keep abreast of developments in the space age. Packed with valuable information and photographs, it is a handsome reference book for everyone interested in today's vital new dimension—the progress of missiles and rockets around the world.

ROCKETS
AROUND THE WORLD

By ERIK BERGAUST

G. P. PUTNAM'S SONS, NEW YORK

FOREWORD

The rocket, once considered a childish toy, is now honored as a vital tool in man's stride toward the stars. Progress in rockets and missiles is zooming ahead, with more and more countries working hard to get in step with the times. Leading the field are the U. S. and Russia. Of the 100 operational rockets and missiles throughout the world, 50 are American, although only 6 of the most recent American ones are included here. Until the launchings of the Sputniks, information on Russian missiles had been scarce. Since then the Soviets have revealed enough details to enable us to draw a fair picture of their strength. I believe that this book contains the most extensive report on Russian missiles ever published in the U. S. As is the case in the U. S., recent missiles in most countries are classified and photographs and technical data unavailable. So, some missiles described in the text are not shown in the picture section.

To prepare this book I needed help from many sources. My thanks go to the Public Information Offices of the U. S. Army, Navy, and Air Force, private sources overseas; *Missiles and Rockets* magazine, and in particular, Mr. Peer Fossen, associate editor of that magazine.

ERIK BERGAUST 1958

To PEER and ERIK RICHARD

MANUFACTURED IN THE UNITED
STATES OF AMERICA

Published simultaneously in the Dominion of
Canada by Longmans, Green & Company, Toronto

CONTENTS

PHOTO CREDITS

G. M. Basford Co., page 4; U. S. Air Force, pages 5, 6; U. S. Navy, page 8; U. S. Army, page 9; British Information Services, pages 33, 34, 35, 37; Convair, pages 6, 7; F. C. Durant, pages 13, 39; 43; Informations Aeronautiques, pages 28, 29; *Missiles and Rockets*, pages 10, 11, 14, 17, 18; Secretariat D'Etat L'Air, page 25; James H. Stevens, pages 33, 36.

JUPITER-C

APPROXIMATE
SPECIFICATIONS:
VELOCITY: 18,000 mph •
RANGE: orbit • PAYLOAD
(WARHEAD): 30.8 pounds
(weight of Explorer) •
LENGTH: 68 feet 7 inches
(over-all) • WEIGHT: 50,000
pounds • TYPE: research rocket
(4 stages) • DIAMETER:
70 inches • GUIDANCE:
inertial • THRUST: 83,000
pounds • PROPELLANT: liquid
propellant (1st stage), solid
propellant (2, 3, & 4 stages)

UNITED STATES

Cape Canaveral, Huntsville, White Sands—magic capitals of America's missile world. Rockets streaking skyward, missiles arching toward target planes. Jupiter, Thor, Atlas—mighty, thundering names that recall powerful, ancient gods. Thus the new science of rockets and missiles gives new meanings to old words, and, moving ahead at a dizzy pace, coins words in flight—retrorocket, ultrasonic, warhead, payload. These words, with their explosive meanings, are working their way into our speech. At first it may seem like a strange and difficult language, but we should meet it head-on.

THOR *APPROXIMATE SPECIFICATIONS: VELOCITY: 10,000 – 12,000 mph • RANGE: 1,500 – 2,300 miles • PAYLOAD (WARHEAD): 600 – 1,000 pounds • LENGTH: 60 feet • WEIGHT: 90,000 – 100,000 pounds • TYPE: surface-to-surface IRBM • DIAMETER: 9 feet • GUIDANCE: inertial • THRUST: 165,000 pounds • PROPELLANT: liquid oxygen & kerosene*

How else can we enjoy our ringside seat at history in the making?

History gives meaning to words, and "Paper Clip" means something special to U. S. missile men. It was the program which sent crack German scientists to the U. S. after World War II. Among them was the brilliant Wernher von Braun, one of the masterminds behind the launching of the first U. S. satellite. "Paper Clip" helped import vital know-how — a solid foundation on which the Army could build a missile program. American industry went to work, creating a need for missile engineers and tech-

ATLAS *APPROXIMATE SPECIFICATIONS: VELOCITY: 12,000 mph • RANGE: 5,500 – 6,300 miles • POWERPLANT: boosters (2) 165,000 pounds thrust sustainer (1) 100,000 pounds thrust • PAYLOAD (WARHEAD): 2,000 pounds estimated • LENGTH: 80 feet • TYPE: surface-to-surface • DIAMETER: 12 feet • GUIDANCE: radio-inertial • PROPELLANT: liquid oxygen & kerosene*

nicians. Since then a whole new industry has grown — based on the experiments with captured V-2s.

Of course, the American missiles didn't shoot into the sky right away. There were setbacks and stalls, starts and stops. In 1946 the Air Force started Project MX-774, a forerunner of the current Atlas Intercontinental Ballistics Missile. A year later the Defense Department classed it an "unnecessary" weapon and the program was canceled. Air Force officers realized that this was a dangerous setback. They had watched the Army prove the worth of ballistics rockets. They knew

that other nations were working on long-range ballistic missiles. Could we do less?

The Air Force felt that eventually it should take charge of the long-range missile. In 1951 Air Force planners proved their case. Now the Air Force controls the Thor Intermediate Bal-

listic Missile and the Atlas and Titan ICBM, as well as different space-flight projects.

In the field of surface-to-surface missiles the Army needs field-artillery missiles to support land, airborne, and amphibious operations. These missiles, carrying appropriate warheads,

VANGUARD

*APPROXIMATE
SPECIFICATIONS:
VELOCITY: 18,000 —19,000
miles per hour • RANGE: orbit
• POWERPLANT: G.E. LP
first stage • Aerojet LP second
stage • Grand Central
solid third stage • PAYLOAD
(WARHEAD): 70 pounds
(weight of satellite & third
stage rocket empty) LENGTH:
72 feet • WEIGHT: 22,000
pounds • TYPE: research rocket
(satellite launcher) •
DIAMETER: 45 inches •
GUIDANCE: inertial •
THRUST: 27,000 pounds •
PROPELLANT: first stage:
kerosene liquid oxygen
second stage: liquid
third stage: solid*

must hit targets beyond the range of conventional artillery. They should be able to destroy tanks and fortifications and to support troops making airborne assaults or armored breakthroughs. The Army has several such missiles, including Redstone, Jupiter, and Pershing.

Rockets and missiles are changing the Navy, too. They have changed naval tactics, equipment, and added to the general efficiency of operations. New unmanned weapons, including super-torpedoes, will extend the defense arms of the Navy. At present the Navy is working on a 1,500-mile

JUPITER

*APPROXIMATE SPECIFICATIONS:
VELOCITY: 10,000 – 12,000 mph •
RANGE: 1,500 miles • PAYLOAD
(WARHEAD): 600 – 1,000 pounds •
LENGTH: 58 feet • WEIGHT:
90,000 – 100,000 pounds • TYPE:
surface-to-surface IRBM • DIAMETER:
8 – 9 feet • GUIDANCE: inertial •
THRUST: 135,000 – 165,000 pounds
• PROPELLANT: liquid oxygen
and kerosene*

Polaris missile, called the Fleet Ballistic Missile.

The Polaris fits into the picture of National Defense as a weapon of retaliation and a deterrent to attack. With it the Navy will be able to reach almost any potential target in the world. And the mobility of ships at sea makes them elusive targets for enemy missiles—a massive retaliatory force for the U. S.

What about *future* rockets and missiles? Will they reach a "ceiling" beyond which they cannot go? The answer lies with new fuels. Twenty years ago a new fuel was likely to in-

SERGEANT

APPROXIMATE SPECIFICATIONS:
VELOCITY: mach 3 • RANGE:
100 – 150 miles • LENGTH: 30 feet
• WEIGHT: 25,000 – 35,000 pounds
• TYPE: surface-to-surface • DIAMETER:
36 inches • GUIDANCE: inertial •
THRUST: 50,000 – 75,000 pounds
• PROPELLANT: solid

crease a rocket thrust by about 25 per cent at a cost of a few dollars. Today the Army is trying to increase thrust power by a few per cent at a greater cost. With present compounds and problems of stability, the best we can hope for is increased efficiency by 25 per cent. This will probably be reached in ten years.

Both the Army and the Air Force are working on atomic rockets, which may someday propel space ships. But for the time being, the hope for better propellants lies with "exotic" fuels. Light metals and hydrides (chemical

compounds) — now in production — offer more powerful thrusts than conventional fuels. Known as "Zip" or "Hi-Cal," these exotics are made up of *boron* and other chemicals. We may yet have to call on the old 20-mule-Borax team to pull us to the moon!

Although details on exotic fuels are just starting to trickle out, it is probably safe to say that the laboratory stage has been completed and that construction plants are being built. Within the next few years, the U. S. will produce exotics by the tons. Then —and only then—better rockets will be built.

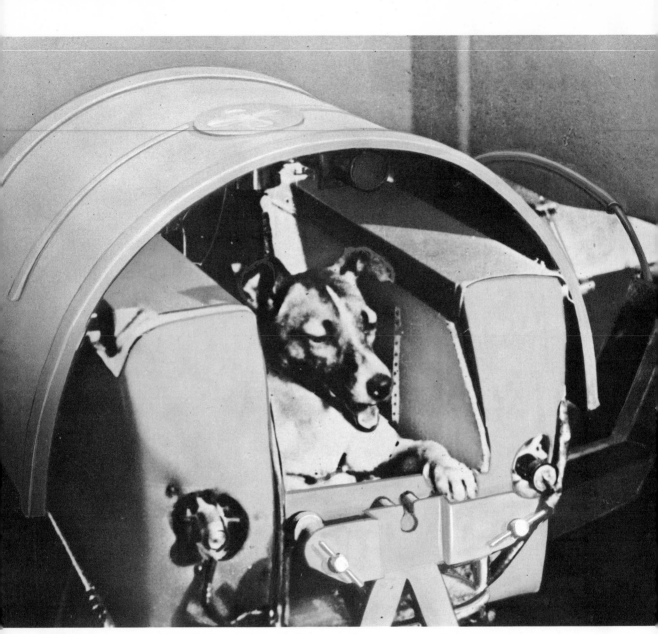

Laika, the Russian Sputnik dog, in her satellite capsule before launching.

SOVIET UNION

The Sputniks spotlighted Russian leadership in the field of missiles. Today the Soviet Union bristles with thousands of missiles of all types and ranges. Their guidance and control equipment is high in quality. Their weapons program is awesome.

The Moscow Rocket Institute, established in 1680, started developing rockets about 1800 — but little was achieved until after World War II. With the capture of Peenemunde — the German rocket base in the Baltic Sea—Russia got many German engi-

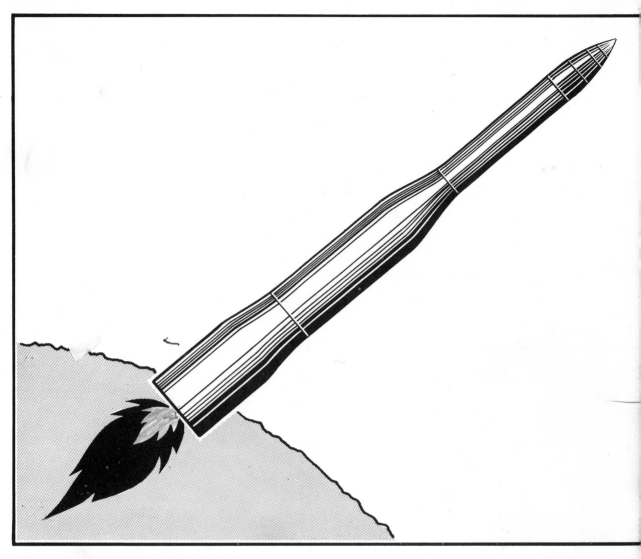

CH 10 (SPUTNIK LAUNCHERS)

APPROXIMATE SPECIFICATIONS: VELOCITY: 18,000 mph • CEILING: 1,000 miles •
POWERPLANT: 1- or 2-stage liquid rockets • PAYLOAD: 1,120 pounds • LENGTH: 118 feet •
TYPE: satellite launcher (Sputnik II) • DIAMETER: 14 feet • GUIDANCE: radio and gyro
stabilization • THRUST: unknown • PROPELLANT: kerosene and liquid oxygen

neers and much equipment. The captured men and materials formed the hard core of their missile program for the next five years.

In this period the Russians built about 1,000 V-2 rockets to get experience and to study conditions in the upper atmosphere. Today Russia no longer leans on the Germans. In 1950 to 1955 most of them were shipped home and Russian equipment replaced German powerplants, missiles, and guidance systems. Since 1955 the Reds have made independent designs.

POL-1

APPROXIMATE
SPECIFICATIONS:
VELOCITY: 3,000 mph •
CEILING: 10 – 15 miles •
POWERPLANT: 4 solid-fuel
boosters, 1 solid-fuel main rocket
• PAYLOAD: 8 pounds •
LENGTH: 13 feet • TYPE: research
rocket • DIAMETER: 0.9 foot
• GUIDANCE: fin stabilized •
THRUST: unknown • PROPELLANT:
solid-fuel

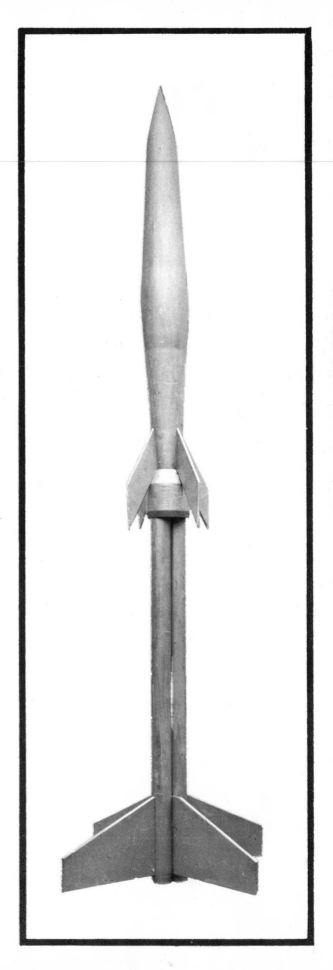

POL-2

APPROXIMATE SPECIFICATIONS:
VELOCITY: 4,000 –5,000 mph •
CEILING: 100 miles • PAYLOAD:
50 – 100 pounds • LENGTH: 22
feet • TYPE: research rocket •
DIAMETER: 2 feet • GUIDANCE:
fin stabilized and gyros • THRUST:
25,000 pounds • PROPELLANT:
kerosene and liquid oxygen

T-6 *APPROXIMATE SPECIFICATIONS: VELOCITY: 1,650 mph • RANGE: 25 miles • CEILING: 72,500 ft. • POWERPLANT: solid propellant rocket • PAYLOAD (WARHEAD): 80 pounds • LENGTH: 10 feet • TYPE: Ballistic rocket • DIAMETER: 5.2 inches • GUIDANCE: ballistic • PROPELLANT: solid fuel*

As with most Russian weapons, the missile program aims at a few standard, reliable weapons rather than an arsenal of many types. Strict censorship held back news about Soviet missiles from 1947 to 1953, but from 1954 limited information has been allowed to pass through the iron curtain. So today it is possible to chart the Red missile program.

It is believed that Russia's ballistic and long-range missile arsenal includes six different types. The T-1, which heads the list, is actually a

15

T-7A *APPROXIMATE SPECIFICATIONS: VELOCITY: 3,000 mph • RANGE: 30 – 60 miles • CEILING: 45 miles • POWERPLANT: liquid rocket • PAYLOAD (WARHEAD): 50 pounds • LENGTH: 26 feet • TYPE: surface-to-surface SRBM • DIAMETER: 2.5 feet • GUIDANCE: unguided (ballistic) • THRUST: 17,600 pounds from 30 – 60 seconds • PROPELLANT: kerosene and liquid oxygen*

German V-2 with improved performance due to use of hotter-burning kerosene instead of alcohol, increased engine-chamber pressure, and weight shaving. This boosted the thrust from 50,000 pounds to 77,000 and increased the range from 200 to 400 miles.

Next came the T-2, a two-stage IRBM with a combined thrust of about 200,000 pounds. From this grew the T-3 ICBM, a top priority missile with 400,000 pounds of thrust.

As a result of the Russian IRBM and ICBM crash programs, the status

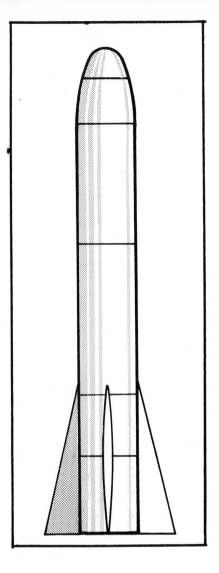

T-2 (M103) *APPROXIMATE SPECIFICATIONS:
VELOCITY: 5,000—6,000 mph • RANGE: 1,800 miles •
CEILING: 300 miles • POWERPLANT: liquid rockets
• PAYLOAD (WARHEAD): 700 pounds • LENGTH:
80 feet (2 stages) • TYPE: surface-to-surface IRBM •
DIAMETER: 10 feet • GUIDANCE: radio-inertial
• THRUST: 1st stage 254,000 & 2nd stage 77,000
pounds • PROPELLANT: kerosene & liquid oxygen*

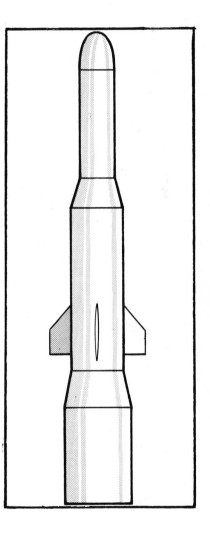

T-3 (M104)

*APPROXIMATE SPECIFICATIONS:
VELOCITY: 15,000 mph • RANGE: 5,000 miles •
CEILING: 600 miles • POWERPLANT: liquid rockets
(3 stages) • PAYLOAD (WARHEAD): 700 pounds
• LENGTH: 110 feet • TYPE: surface-to-surface ICBM
• DIAMETER: 15 feet • GUIDANCE: radio-inertial
• THRUST: 1st stage 400,000 pounds; 2nd stage
77,000 pounds; 3rd stage unknown • PROPELLANT:
kerosene (with exotic additives) and liquid oxygen*

of the A4(T-4), a winged glide missile, is not known. Perhaps it has been set aside. And there's little information on the T-4A, a rocket-powered, manned glide bomber.

In the low-range ballistic missile field, the T-7A with a range of 30-60 miles is one of the Red Army's main weapons. This is a solid-propellant rocket with nuclear capabilities for tactical use. Some versions of it have been in the hands of the Polish and East German armies for a long time.

In the anti-aircraft field the Rus-

J-3 *APPROXIMATE SPECIFICATIONS: VELOCITY: 800 mph • RANGE: 500 miles • CEILING: 45,000 feet • POWERPLANT: turbojet and rocket booster • PAYLOAD (WARHEAD): 600 pounds • LENGTH: 35 feet • TYPE: ship or surface-to-surface • WING SPAN: 22 feet • GUIDANCE: radio/radar • THRUST: 3,000 – 4,000 pounds • PROPELLANT: jet fuel*

sians placed the M-1 missile into operation several years ago. A superior missile in this category is the T-7, designed to defend Russia from attacks by bombers. For low-altitude targets the Reds use the T-8 barrage *flak-rocket* system. Two other flak rockets, the T-6 and the GVAI, use solid propellants. The standard air-to-air missile is the 3.2-inch rocket. Like the U. S. Mighty Mouse (a 2.75-inch folding-fin aircraft rocket), it is patterned after the German R4M. The M-100 guided aircraft rocket has been

M-2 *APPROXIMATE SPECIFICATIONS: VELOCITY: 1,800 mph • RANGE: 40 miles • CEILING: 40 miles • POWERPLANT: 2 solid-fuel rockets • PAYLOAD (WARHEAD): 25 pounds • LENGTH: 22 feet • TYPE: surface-to-air (anti-aircraft) • DIAMETER: 1.5 feet • GUIDANCE: radar and infra-red homing • THRUST: unknown • PROPELLANT: solid-fuel*

radically streamlined and cut in weight. And it appears that the new M-100A is small enough so that several can be carried by a jet interceptor along with 3.2-inch rockets.

The Soviet Navy also carries a heavy load of missiles. According to experts, the growing Russian submarine fleet (about 100 under construction and 400–600 in operation) could isolate Europe and hit most of the U. S. and Canada with ballistic rockets. In addition, vigorous work is being done on cruise missiles.

T-1 (M101)

APPROXIMATE SPECIFICATIONS:
VELOCITY: 4,300 mph • RANGE: 400 miles •
CEILING: 150 miles • POWERPLANT: liquid rocket
• PAYLOAD (WARHEAD): 800 pounds •
LENGTH: 46 feet • TYPE: surface-to-surface IRBM
• DIAMETER: 5 – 6 feet • GUIDANCE: radio-inertial,
ballistic • THRUST: 77,000 pounds •
PROPELLANT: kerosene and liquid oxygen

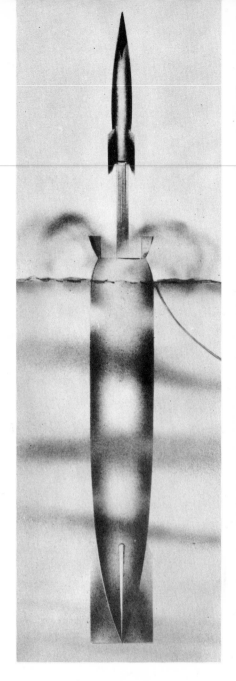

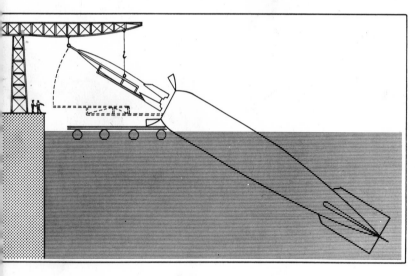

The Red Navy has missile ships as well as fast, modern destroyers. Anti-aircraft missile ships have been sighted in the Baltic and the Pacific together with short- and medium-range missile attack vessels.

With Peenemunde the Russians took charge of a fabulous weapons system: submersible missile-launching platforms designed to be towed by submarines. It took the Germans—with a wartime crash program—only two years to develop missile launchers and it seems obvious that the Russians

COMET (1&2)

APPROXIMATE SPECIFICATIONS:
VELOCITY: 3,000 – 4,000 miles •
Range: Comet 1: 90 – 100 miles
Comet 2: 500 – 700 miles •
CEILING: 40 miles • POWERPLANT: solid-fuel
rocket and torpedo booster • PAYLOAD
(WARHEAD): 1,000 pounds • LENGTH 33 feet
• TYPE: submarine-to-surface target •
DIAMETER: 3.8 feet • GUIDANCE: unknown •
THRUST: unknown • PROPELLANT: solid fuel

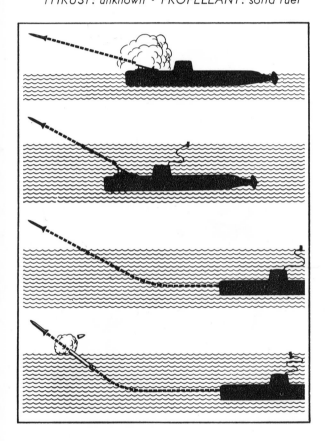

have improved on these. Although the Comet-1 and Comet-2 missiles were developed specifically for undersea launching, longer-range missiles (up to 1,500 miles) may be used. Red sub-launched missiles could strike any target in the world.

SE 4300

APPROXIMATE SPECIFICATIONS:
VELOCITY: near 760 mph • RANGE: 12 miles
• POWERPLANT: liquid rocket • WEIGHT:
2,200 pounds • TYPE: surface-to-air
training vehicle (Nike-type) •
DIAMETER: 18 inches • GUIDANCE: unknown

FRANCE

read 22-29

After World War II, France shot into the forefront of world rocketry, although not climbing to the high level of the U. S. and the U. S. S. R. It's hard to track down the exact beginnings of French work in the field. But they have been fascinated by rockets and space travel for a long time.

Three hundred years ago French writer Cyrano de Bergerac wrote a story in which rockets were used to fly to the moon. His space traveler sat in a box and was shot into space by skyrockets. Fiction is often years and years ahead of facts.

During World War I, France was

MASALCA

APPROXIMATE SPECIFICATIONS: French Navy surface-to-air missile. Details not available.

the only nation to fire rockets in combat. She used surface-to-air incendiaries and the Le Prieur rocket—carried by airplane — against German Zeppelins and balloons. The catapult-launched SSM Torpille, a crude flying bomb, appeared in 1915. This was the V-1 of World War I, and carried a payload of 440 pounds. From 1914 on, the French also used 27- and 34-millimeter rockets—and in 1941 tested the EA-41 right under the noses of the Germans. Immediately after the war this ten-foot-long unguided missile flew 35 miles with a maximum thrust of 2,200 pounds.

Today French missiles fall into six categories: air-to-air, air-to-surface,

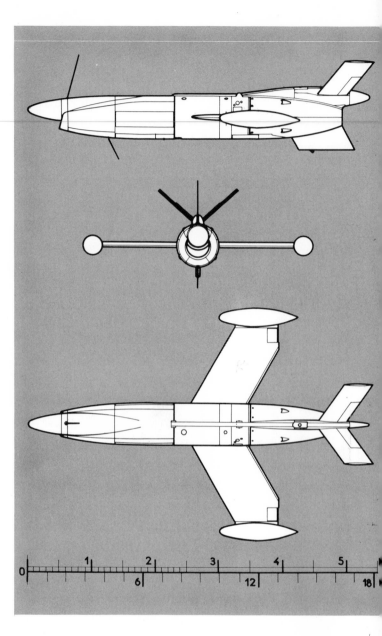

C.T. 20

APPROXIMATE SPECIFICATIONS:
VELOCITY: 560 mph • RANGE: 125
miles • CEILING: 40,000 feet •
POWERPLANT: turbojet plus two solid
powder take-off rockets • LENGTH:
17.71 feet • TAKE-OFF WEIGHT:
1,470 pounds • DIAMETER: 2.16 feet
• TYPE: target drone • WING AREA:
34.34 square feet • SPAN: 11.15
feet • GUIDANCE: radio •
THRUST: 880 pounds

surface-to-air, surface-to-surface, drone and special test vehicles, and upper-atmosphere sounding rockets.

They have eight air-to-air missiles. The Matra M.04 is a smaller model of an earlier surface-to-air and air-to-surface missile. Liquid propellants give the rocket 2,750 pounds of thrust for 14 seconds. It's all metal, with a

duralumin skin and gyro-controlled tail vanes. It made tests at the Sahara desert ranges. Matra also produces the AA.20 and R.051. The AA.20 is accurate, liquid-propelled, and carried by Mystère A and B fighters. The R.051 is solid-propelled — and highly accurate. It features a *proximity fuse* and *canard construction*. Range is

believed to be considerable.

Other important missiles are the M.510, a two-stage type, and the M.-511, which is cloaked in secrecy but may be used on the Trident rocket-powered plane. Currently the French are pushing the SPECMAS 5103. Like the Matra R.051, it carries a powerful warhead armed with *proximity fuse*.

It probably rides a beam to the target.

The French haven't done much in the air-to-surface category, or are keeping what they have done under wraps. Some of their air-to-air missiles can double as ASMs, especially the short-range SS.10 and SS.11, which are fired from helicopters. The BB.10, their latest guided bomb, is

VERONIQUE *APPROXIMATE SPECIFICATIONS:*
*VELOCITY: 3,200 mph • ALTITUDE: 84 miles • POWERPLANT: liquid rocket • PAYLOAD
(WARHEAD): not available • LENGTH: 24 feet • DIAMETER: 20 inches • WEIGHT: 3,180
pounds • TYPE: upper atmosphere research vehicle • THRUST: 8,820 pounds*

used with the Vautour fighter bomber.

The French designed their surface-to-air missiles for defense against air attacks; most of these models are in the experimental stage. Leading types are the Sud-Est (now Sud-Aviation) 4300 and LRBA-DEFA's Parca. The 4300 was developed from the 4100, a liquid-sustained, solid-boosted type.

According to the French, the 4300 performs like the American Nike. It's tail-less and has 45° swept-back wings. A liquid-propelled missile, it's now used for training purposes. The Parca has a range of about 12 miles and can bring down aircraft up to about a 6-mile altitude. It's a beam rider with *proximity fuse and canard controls.*

PARCA

APPROXIMATE SPECIFICATIONS: VELOCITY: mach 1.7 • RANGE: 12 – 14 miles • POWERPLANT: liquid rocket • LENGTH: 14.7 feet • WEIGHT: 2,200 pounds • TYPE: surface-to-air missile • GUIDANCE: beam rider

Surface - to - surface research has centered on anti-tank weapons—with notable success. Both the Army and Air Force have taken part, the latter being interested in helicopter-to-surface missiles. The SS.10 program incorporates the SFECMAS 5200 series and the DEFA's Entac, both with nearly identical ranges and speeds. (The 5202 is a trainer, the 5203 the operational vehicle.) They are *wire-guided*, solid-propelled, with *shaped charges* to pierce thick tank skins. The 5200 saw action in the Israel-Egypt war with good results. Commands are relayed along wires which unwind under the wings. The Entac version is now in production.

SS. 10

APPROXIMATE SPECIFICATIONS:
VELOCITY: 190 mph • RANGE: 1.24 miles •
POWERPLANT: solid rocket • LENGTH: 2 feet 10
inches • DIAMETER: 6.3 inches • WEIGHT:
35 pounds • TYPE: anti-tank, close support rocket.
Also used from helicopters at low altitudes •
GUIDANCE: wire

The SS.10 is very accurate and needs only a small crew to operate. Tests show 98 per cent accuracy, and it's significant that the U. S. Army has adopted the design for its own use. The French have fired this missile from helicopters and, reportedly, from twin-engined transports and support airplanes.

Under large-scale production for the Army and Air Force, the SS.11 (SFECMAS 5210) is a long-range version of the SS.10. In addition to SSM and ASM applications, it may be tried out in an air-to-air role.

Other French SSM projects include the BTZ-411.01 bazooka-type missile, the 33-pound Lutin infantry ramjet,

The accurate and versatile SS. 10 needs only a small crew and may be fired from Jeeps, helicopters and transport planes as well as support aircraft.

and the Ogree 1 long-range photo-reconnaissance ramjet vehicle. The latter carries a liquid rocket booster and is tail-less with barrel-type *coleopter rings*.

The only known moderate-range vehicle being worked on by France is the SE.4200, designed to carry a powerful charge about 60 miles. It's launched by solid booster from a ramp mounted on a truck. The French hope that this tail-less guided missile will replace long-range artillery. At the moment there are only rumors of longer-range SSMs under development in France. Advancement belongs to the future, and in missiledom the future is often only a week away.

GREAT BRITAIN | CANADA AUSTRALIA

Is Britain's missile program lagging? Until recently the answer would have been yes. Yet the British have been testing missiles for many years, but keeping the results a secret. A short time ago information released by the Ministry of Supply showed that Britain has a more advanced program than was generally realized.

Four hundred British companies are working in the missile field. The more notable are Bristol Aircraft, Ltd., English Electric Co., De Havilland Aircraft, Ltd., A. V. Roe, Fairey Aviation and Vickers-Armstrongs.

Great Britain announced last February the development of a medium-range ballistic rocket more advanced than the American IRBMs now in production. It will be launched from underground sites. Marked "top priority" and developed in close co-operation with the U. S., it probably will carry a nuclear warhead.

The Fireflash, Britain's first air-to-air missile, dates back to World War II. This weapon is unique because it has no sustainer motor. Solid-propellant boosters of the wrap-around type accelerate it to maximum speed and then separate, allowing the missile to coast to target. It uses a Marconi beam-rider guidance system.

The Fireflash, now a training weapon for the Fighter Command, also features countermeasures against enemy jamming. The main body is tubular with cruciform wings and *guide vanes.*

Another air-to-air weapon is the Firestreak. It relies on *passive homing* through an *infra-red seeker.* Conventionally designed, the missile has cross-shaped wings and fins. It is larger than the Fireflash because it carries a motor inside its body. Because of the nature of the infra-red wave lengths, the nosecap is eight-sided to provide distortion-free "seeking" panels. The Firestreak, powered by a solid-propellant motor, should be delivered to the RAF late in 1958, and will be made available to friendly nations.

Research vehicles such as RTV, GPV, and MTV sparked Britain's surface-to-air missile program, leading to weapons like the Bloodhound, Thunderbird, and Sea Slug, now in production.

The Bloodhound has been under development since 1949. Two Thor ramjet engines—mounted above and below the fuselage — supply sustaining power. Solid propellants boost the missile to operating speed at the rate of 1,500 feet per second. At the front of the mounting pylons of each ramjet is an intake for ram-air, fuel, and hydraulic turbopumps. The Bloodhound has a blunt body, a pointed, archlike nose, stubby wings and rectangular fixed tail. Unlike a symmetrical, cross-shaped missile, the Bloodhound banks

JINDIVIK APPROXIMATE SPECIFICATIONS: CEILING: 50,000 feet •
POWERPLANT: Viper jet turbine • PAYLOAD (WARHEAD): not available • LENGTH: 22
feet • WING SPAN: 19 feet • TYPE: target drone, originally planned as interceptor missile.
Also being studied for surface-to-surface missions • GUIDANCE: radio • THRUST: 1,600 pounds
• PROPELLANT: jet fuel

and turns by elevator action. Speed is supersonic. The Bloodhound, Britain's first surface-to-air missile, uses an excellent radar control system which can be adapted to other SAMs now in production.

Another SAM, the Thunderbird, should soon reach full production. It's a beam rider with a main powerplant and four wrap-around solid-propellant boosters to provide launching thrust. Liquid propellants powered some of the earlier versions, but late models feature solid propellants. Design is "classical"— a cylinder with

a nose like a cone, with tapered wings and tail-control blades. There's little information available on the Thunderbird, but British sources guess its length at about 20 feet and diameter at 15 inches. It differs from the Bloodhound, for it carries its own radar system. Built along the lines of the American Nike-Hercules, Thunderbird's performance is expected to equal its American counterpart.

According to official releases, the Royal Navy's only contribution to the missile field is the Sea Slug. Designed as a defensive weapon, it started sea

BLOODHOUND

APPROXIMATE SPECIFICATIONS:
VELOCITY: supersonic • RANGE: unknown •
POWERPLANT: ramjets and rocket boosters •
PAYLOAD (WARHEAD): unknown • LENGTH:
22 feet • TYPE: surface-to-air • DIAMETER:
1 foot 9 inches • GUIDANCE: combination of
beam and homing systems • THRUST: unknown •
PROPELLANT: liquid (not known) and
solid-fuel boosters

trials about a year ago aboard the Girdle Ness, a guided-weapons ship. The missile is possibly in the medium-range class, has movable fins with large rectangular wings. Like the Fireflash, the Sea Slug has wrap-around solid-fuel boosters. Sea Slugs are launched from triple launchers by remote control.

Britain hasn't named its first guided missile in the air-to-surface field, but, according to reports, A. V. Roe will build the first model. The British call this kind of vehicle a "stand-off bomb." Until the development of ICBMs, the vehicle will be carried by RAF Vulcan and Victor bombers.

Although Britain got an early start in the surface-to-surface field with the Aerial Target, a 1916 guided airplane, very little else has been developed until recently. After firing some V-2s from Cuxhaven, Germany, all activity

32

FIREFLASH

APPROXIMATE SPECIFICATIONS:
VELOCITY: supersonic • RANGE:
unknown • POWERPLANT: solid-
propellant rockets • PAYLOAD
(WARHEAD): unknown • LENGTH:
90 inches • TYPE: air-to-air •
WING SPAN: 28 inches •
GUIDANCE: beam rider
• THRUST: unknown •
PROPELLANT: solid fuel

THUNDERBIRD

APPROXIMATE SPECIFICATIONS:
VELOCITY: supersonic • CEILING:
20 – 30 miles • POWERPLANT:
solid rocket plus boosters •
PAYLOAD (WARHEAD): unknown
• LENGTH: 22 feet • TYPE: surface-
to-air • GUIDANCE: beam rider
• THRUST: unknown •
PROPELLANT: solid fuel

seemed to stop. Today the only work along these lines is being done by De Havilland. Along with Rolls Royce, De Havilland is working on a 2,000-mile IRBM for the RAF. Until the IRBM is airborne, the U. S. Honest John will be used for training and the U. S. Corporal for bombardment. In the smaller SSMs, Fairey Aviation is developing an anti-tank weapon. This probably will be used for air-to-ground purposes, too.

CANADA

To a large extent the Canadian missile arsenal is a collection of odds and ends from the U. S. and Great Britain. Canada has done some original work in the field but has yet to develop a missile.

Canadians started to build an air-to-air missile—the Velvet Glove—in 1951. But five years and 25 million dollars later the project was dropped because of a change in government

BOBBIN *Firings at the Woomera test range in South Australia have produced successful results. The above photographs show a complete test cycle of Britain's Bobbin. The British test most of their missiles at Woomera. The Bobbin is a ramjet test vehicle powered by Thor motors. The missile can be examined after firing and rebuilt for repeated use. At the nose of the missile is a spike on which it lands, parachutes having slowed down the speed of descent.*

policy. Even today a security blanket shrouds all but a few minor details of the weapon.

But Canadian industry gained first-hand missile knowledge from the Velvet Glove project. The Royal Canadian Air Force has acquired valuable know-how in testing and firing ballistic missiles and has established effective facilities for handling any future weapons. A ground-test ballistic range at Valcartier, Quebec, can make res-

onance studies, speed tests and the like. Canada has a short-range test-firing station—Point Petre Range—near the Royal Canadian Artillery center at Petawa, Ontario, and close to the RCAF base at Trenton. RCAF Station Cold Lake, Alberta, played a major role in the air firing tests of Velvet Glove. This base, planned to replace World War II ranges, is one of the most modern testing establishments in the world. Station Cold Lake,

operated by RCAF Air Defense Command, is home base for the Weapons Training Unit and the Central Experimental and Proving Establishment. The station also operates a practice range about 30 miles north of Cold Lake.

Great Britain and the U. S. frequently test operational missiles with the Canadian Armed Forces, and several hundred Canadians have visited U. S. Army missile centers. The U. S. and Britain have loaned up-to-date material on missiles and atomic research to Canada. Exchange agreements between the countries keep Canada's scientists abreast of developments in these fields. Currently, Canada is negotiating with the U. S. for production of the Sparrow 2, which probably will go into production this year.

FIRESTREAK

APPROXIMATE SPECIFICATIONS: VELOCITY: supersonic • RANGE: unknown • CEILING: launched by high-altitude fighter planes which can fly above 40,000 feet • POWERPLANT: solid-fuel rocket • PAYLOAD (WARHEAD): unknown • LENGTH: 10 feet • TYPE: air-to-air • DIAMETER: 1 foot • GUIDANCE: infra-red passive homing • THRUST: unknown • PROPELLANT: solid fuel

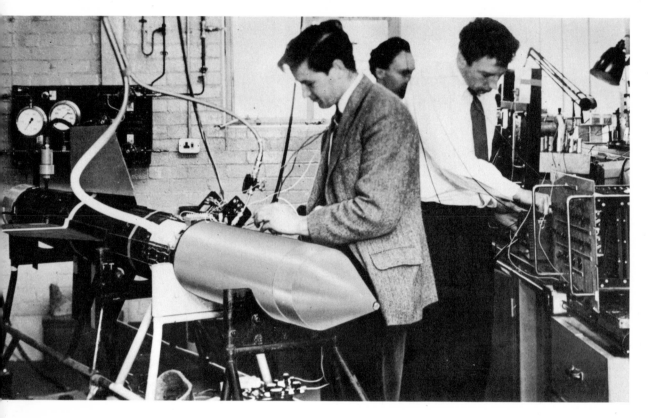

AUSTRALIA

Highlights from "Down Under" show a unique situation : a large country to defend and only 10 million people to supply the money. Australian industry can't cope with complex missile programs or hope to play a top role in any developments in the near future. As a member of the British Commonwealth of Nations on the one hand and part of the Southeast Asian

Treaty Organization on the other, Australia needs tactical missiles, particularly for air defense. But in spite of limitations the Aussies are making a contribution to Western missile progress.

To date, Australia's main contribution is the Jindivik, a subsonic pilotless aircraft capable of altitudes of 50,000 feet plus. Originally thought of as an interceptor missile, it is used primarily now as a target drone.

SEA SLUG

APPROXIMATE SPECIFICATIONS: VELOCITY: subsonic • RANGE: unknown • CEILING: 65,000 feet • POWERPLANT: solid-fuel rocket and boosters • PAYLOAD (WARHEAD): unknown • LENGTH: 19.5 feet • DIAMETER: 20 inches • TYPE: ship-to-air • WEIGHT: 2,200 pounds • GUIDANCE: unknown • PROPELLANT: solid fuel

Studies are currently under way to determine whether it can operate as a surface-to-surface missile of the Matador-Regulus type. Recently, Australia sold ten Jindiviks — complete with ground control equipment and space parts — to the Swedish Armed Forces, who will test them with new Swedish SAMs and AAMs.

A big headache for Australia is the defense of its major cities, especially Sidney. For defense purposes it is studying missiles like the U. S. Talos and Nike and Britain's Bloodhound. Cost and availability, as well as ability, will determine the choice of missile. Target date for ringing Australian cities with missiles is sometime in 1959. In the air-to-air field the Royal Australian Air Force prefers Britain's Firestreak, which could be manufactured Down Under. Local companies already produce some of its parts.

SWITZERLAND

The Swiss missile industry and the large Oerlikon manufacturing concern of Switzerland fit together like one of the country's famous watches. In fact, they're almost the same. Oerlikon applies the same high standards to missiles as it did to conventional weapons. The company now produces missiles for Switzerland and various foreign countries. Two of its outstanding missiles are the Type 50 series SAM and the Cobra series anti-tank rocket.

Development of the Type 50 anti-aircraft weapon started shortly after World War II. The Type 54 is a slim, streamlined, rocket-propelled weapon capable of intercepting aircraft up to about 50,000 feet. Fired from a twin launcher, it is about 20 feet long, with a diameter of 16 inches and launching weight of 770 pounds. It has two sets of cruciform wings of sandwich construction. The main (forward) set give it the necessary lift for controlled flight, then move forward to adjust for the center-of-gravity shift during the power stage. The rear set of wings are used for *gas-jet steering* after burn-out, which happens at about 30,000 feet. The missile's liquid-propelled system gives a thrust of about 2,200 pounds for 30 seconds. Propellant supply is compressed nitrogen gas. For smooth ignition, the 54 uses a starting fuel of triethylamine and xylidine. No booster unit is used.

The Type 54 is a beam rider. Ground units operate a radar target-tracker and guidance beam path simultaneously. The radar tracker feeds information to the missile guidance beam, which steers the weapon to target. *A proximity fuse* fires the warhead if the missile doesn't hit the target. This weapon system is complete and has been available to other countries for about three years. In addition to Switzerland, Italy and Sweden are using the Type 54, and Japan has acquired a license to make the weapon. The Type 56 is an improved version, and a later model, the Type 57, is under development.

The Cobra anti-tank weapon, a wire-guided, solid-propelled rocket, closely resembles the French SS.10 and Entac. All these weapons are based on the German X-4, a World War II development. Weighing about 24 pounds (about one tenth as large as the U. S. Dart), maximum range is about 190 miles. Like the shorter-range Bazooka, the Cobra features an armor-piercing shaped-charge warhead.

Other outstanding weapons— though unguided — are the 5-centimeter and 8-centimeter FF (forward-

OERLIKON-54

APPROXIMATE SPECIFICATIONS: VELOCITY: 1,026 mph • RANGE: 15.5 miles • CEILING: 50,000 feet plus • POWERPLANT: liquid rocket • PAYLOAD (WARHEAD): not available • LENGTH: 19.7 feet • SPAN: 4.25 feet • WEIGHT: 772 pounds • TYPE: surface-to-air missile • DIAMETER: 16 inches • GUIDANCE: beam rider • THRUST: 2,200 pounds • PROPELLANT: kerosene plus nitric acid

firing, folding-fin) rockets. These highly effective air-to-surface rockets have been developed for the Gloster Meteor and Venom aircraft. They carry a shaped-charge warhead which explodes as it hits target. A *proximity fuse* is being developed. Electric power to operate a miniature radar unit will come from a gas turbine. The warhead fires the moment the radar signal, reflected from the target, begins to weaken.

SWEDEN

The largest, most advanced Scandinavian country, Sweden ranks third as a European power today (after Great Britain and France). Not being a NATO member, she plays a significant role in the cold war. She could very well upset the plans for an atom-free, de-missiled zone across Scandinavia. In planning this zone, the U. S. and Russia obviously have overlooked or underestimated Sweden's progress in missiles and nuclear research. Intensive research is reported to have been carried out by large Swedish weapons concerns in co-operation with the Swedish defense department. Scandinavian sources say that Swedish nuclear scientists have broken through—on their own initiative—to develop missiles with atomic warheads.

Sweden's missile activity includes many areas, but reportedly not IRBMs and ICBMs. The main emphasis has been on SAMs and missiles for coastal defense. Work on other types has been underway for some time, but not with the high priority placed on aircraft-interceptor weapons in the Bomarc and Nike classes. Surface-to-surface missiles have been under study for naval use, but have not been applied to land operations.

Bofors (famous maker of World War II anti-aircraft guns) has developed a guided AAM for the J35 interceptor. The SAAB A32 Lansen, an all-weather attack aircraft, also can handle Swedish ASMs for tactical strikes. One of these fighter missiles is the Jaktrobot (Type 304—BO4), due for use soon. The Sjorobot (sea missile) is aimed toward surface-to-surface use. These weapons may be fitted with nuclear warheads. The 304 is undergoing extensive trials before being introduced to service. Production is handled by the Air Force's central workshop and civil contractors.

Sweden has revealed little technical information on the 304, except that it's rocket-powered and carries an all-weather guidance system. A highly regarded weapon in Sweden's defense against naval attack, it will enable Lansen units to fire accurately against vessels well outside the range of conventional artillery.

In addition to the 304, the 315—a new naval surface-to-surface missile —has been designed for use from destroyer-type vessels against enemy craft. This 26-foot-long missile, now undergoing trials at sea, first will equip the destroyers Smaaland and Halland. Four built-in booster rockets shoot it to flight speed. A special jet engine — presumably an advanced pulsejet — supplies cruising power. Like the 304, the 315 has an all-weather guidance system. Its main advantage is that it exceeds the range of conventional naval or coast artillery.

304 (B04)

*APPROXIMATE
SPECIFICATIONS:
VELOCITY: 800 – 1,000 mph •
RANGE: 25 – 50 miles •
POWERPLANT: solid rocket
• PAYLOAD (WARHEAD):
30 pounds • LENGTH: 13 feet •
TYPE: air-to-surface missile
• DIAMETER: 18 inches •
GUIDANCE: all-weather guidance
(infra-red) • THRUST: unknown
• PROPELLANT: solid fuel*

41

JAPAN

Toward the end of the war in the Pacific, Japanese Kamikaze squadrons, diving suicidally from the skies, kept the U. S. Navy constantly alert. The Baka, a rocket-propelled bomb, belonged to the Kamikaze group. She was carried aloft by a Mitsubishi bomber, released near the target, and steered in by a pilot who had been sealed in his seat. The Baka was a hair-raising weapon, but outside of this flying bomb, Japan's wartime rocketry program was minor. Apparently, work with liquid propellants was limited to developing a power-plant for the Shusui airplane, which was in the design stage in 1944-45.

For ten years after the war Japanese rocket research was at a standstill, forbidden by the U. S. But throughout the postwar period Japanese scientists kept abreast of developments in the rest of the world, so they were prepared when rocketry could be carried out again.

Today, Japan has a well-co-ordinated program and is working hard to get to the forefront of space sci-

ences. Activities center around military rocketry, research rocketry, and space-flight planning.

In the military rocket field, Japan is negotiating with the U. S. for missiles, especially those in the Nike class. She is also interested in Swiss and Italian weapons, and now is manufacturing Switzerland's Type 54 on a license basis. Japan also has imported the Italian Airone, a surface-to-surface missile.

The Japanese research-rocket program stemmed from the decision of the National Science Council of Japan to take part in upper atmosphere observations during the International Geophysical Year. The Japanese decided to use *sounding rockets* to climb above the altitudes reached by research balloons. A four-to-five-year plan was mapped out. Two preliminary programs, Pencil and Baby, were started to test rocket designs. The Pencil, nine inches long and 0.7 inch thick, weighed one-half pound, including the solid-propellant motor. Japan manufactured and fired 150 of these rockets at an average cost of $15.

With the experience gained from testing the Pencil, a larger rocket—the Baby—was designed. Four to five feet long, not including a short booster rocket, this weighed about 20 pounds. There were three major types: Baby-S (Simple), Baby-T (Telemetering), and Baby-R (Recovery). Six Baby-S rockets were fired in August, 1955, only seven months after the beginning

BABY SERIES

APPROXIMATE SPECIFICATIONS: VELOCITY: 900 mph • CEILING: 2.5 miles • POWERPLANT: solid fuel motors • LENGTH: 4 – 5 feet (plus short booster rocket) • WEIGHT: 20 pounds • DIAMETER: 3 inches • TYPE: Research • Baby-S for launching stability and dispersion • Baby-T for rocket telemetering systems • Baby-R for recovery

of the basic studies. These firings checked launching stability and dispersion. One month later, six Baby-Ts zoomed upward, to enable scientists to study rocket - telemetering systems. During the following two months, Japan launched — and recovered — Baby-R rockets. The Pencil and Baby tests helped to develop rocket design and telemetering systems.

The high-altitude sounding rocket program incorporates the Kappa, Sigma and Omega projects. The Kappa project, now under development, includes the Kappa-3—a two-stage vehicle—and the Kappa-4 and Kappa-5

KAPPA III

APPROXIMATE SPECIFICATIONS:
VELOCITY: 2,880 mph • RANGE: 16 miles
(70° launching angle) • CEILING: 80,000 feet
(70° launching angle) • POWERPLANT: solid-fuel
rocket • PAYLOAD: 18 pounds • LENGTH: 17
feet • WEIGHT: 370 pounds • DIAMETER:
main rocket: 5.1 inches • booster rocket: 8.9 inches
• TYPE: two-stage sounding rocket

—both three-stage vehicles. Firings have taken place at Michikawa Beach, where the Tokyo University Rocket Research Center conducts tests. Launched at an angle, the Kappa-3s have a top speed of Mach 3.7, a firing time of 143 seconds, and a range of about 20 miles. Kappa-52, used in the IGY program, are designed for altitudes of about 80 miles. An intermediate rocket, Kappa-4, is 16 feet long and can reach the speed of Mach 5, soaring up to 40 miles. Still in the study stage, the Omega project aims at altitudes over 150 miles.

ITALY

Since the end of World War II, Italians have shown a lot of interest in rockets. Unfortunately, little money, lack of co-ordinated work by industry, and the absence of a clear-cut government program have delayed development. Today, Italy has a missile program, and although its structure is a secret we can point to its general outline.

Immediate attention centers on foreign missiles; the first units to be armed will use Nike-Ajax. At least three battalions will get this weapon before 1959. Plans call for these weapons to supply partial protection for three important cities — Rome (the capital), Naples (NATO headquarters), and Milan (the economic center).

In addition to receiving Nike-Ajax from the U. S., Italy wants to build weapons under license from foreign countries. Swiss Oerlikon has granted the first license for its SAM Type 54.

The Italian government also is interested in the U. S. Nike-Hercules, Britain's Bloodhound, and the U. S. Terrier. These weapons may serve with the Italian Navy. According to reports, Britain is willing to sell the Fireflash and the Firestreak; the U. S. may be willing to supply the Falcon and the Sidewinder.

Italy has a modest experimental weapons program. Several government agencies, industrial companies and private groups are working on research and development. There are numerous engineers working on ideas, but lack of money is keeping missiles close to the ground.

One original Italian weapon is the A.R.14, a beam-riding liquid-propelled missile with a range of over 65,000 feet. It is 23 feet long and weighs 1,100 pounds. Its nitric-acid and kerosene-burning engine generates 2,200 pounds of thrust for 29 seconds. Another program is developing the C.7, an infra-red-guided AAM. It is a small, solid-propelled rocket fitted with a rectangular wing. The C.7 coasts for the greater part of flight, maneuvering by altering the angle of its wings. It has not been tested against targets or drones, so its efficiency is not known.

A third Italian effort is the Icaro, a ballistic missile understood to use ramjet power. Reportedly, it plays the same role as the U. S. Honest John with which the Italian Army will be supplied.

Italy has developed various types of unguided rockets, and has even exported an inexpensive model to Japan —the Airone, a solid-propelled, surface-to-surface missile that has a range of over six miles. Another unguided rocket, the Robotti, has been ordered by the Armed Forces. It is about 16 feet long and flies at supersonic speeds. Finally there is the Katyuscia multi-barrel rocket, which has been adopted by the Dutch and Egyptian Armies.

The Language of Rockets and Missiles

Aerodynamic Missile—A vehicle with wings and surfaces like an airplane.

Ballistic Missile—A missile powered only in first stages of flight. Then, like an artillery shell, it follows a curving course to target.

Beam Rider—A missile that follows a beam to the target.

Bird—Slang for missile or rocket.

Booster—The engine that lifts a missile or rocket off the ground.

Booster Cutoff—The moment when a missile's booster or auxiliary unit burns out or drops off.

Burnout—The moment at which a rocket burns out.

Canard Construction—Missile design using a set of small wings or surfaces mounted in the nose section of the vehicle. The canard stabilizing fins are used in connection with the missile's main control surfaces and wings.

Coleopter Rings—Circular or ring-shaped rigid, control surface around a missile body, giving lift much the same as ordinary wings.

Delta-winged—Wings shaped like the Greek letter Delta: $\triangle$.

Duraluminum—A light, strong aluminum alloy.

Enemy Jamming — Radio transmitting used by a defender to upset radio guidance in an attacking missile (using the same frequency as that of the missile), to explode the missile prematurely or to alter its course.

Drone—A target aircraft or missile.

Flak Rocket—Missile used against attacking aircraft and missiles; also anti-aircraft missile.

Gas-Jet Steering — Guidance technique using pressurized air or gas to steer the missile; ordinarily used with a course-correcting system.

Guidance—The steering device of a missile—its "brain."

Guide Vanes—Small control vanes or "rudders" mounted in the exhaust stream of a rocket for guidance and course-correcting of the missile itself.

Guided Missile — Any unmanned vehicle or projectile capable of being directed through the air or space—even into or through the water.

Gyro-Controlled—The use of a gyroscope to stabilize a missile's flight by counteracting roll or tilt.

Hardware—The finished product—a rocket or missile — completed and ready to go.

Inertial Guidance — A complicated guidance system whose instruments "feel" the forces acting on the missile —speed, direction, heat, etc. This information is computed electronically to determine course.

Infra-red Seeker—A guidance method operating on the detection of heat (radiation) waves from a target. Sensitive instruments in the nose of the rocket or missile pick up the heat waves (such as engine exhaust), and through a control system guide it to the target.

Jet—A combustion engine which depends on an outside source of air to operate, unlike a rocket which carries its own oxygen.

Lox—Liquid oxygen.

Mach—The speed of sound, about 760 MPH at sea level.

Multistage Rocket — Several rockets hooked together to fire in succession. As one burns out the next fires.

Nose Cone — The front section of a missile or rocket, for carrying payload.

Oxidizer—The source of oxygen for burning in an engine.

Pad—The base from which a missile or rocket is launched.

Passive Homing—A guidance method where the missile uses self-contained systems to find the target—without any influence from equipment on the ground or in the launching aircraft.

Payload — Instruments carried in a rocket's nose.

Pound of Thrust — The unit of force generated by expanding gas in a jet or rocket motor.

Propellant—Liquid or solid. *Solid propellant:* a powder compound, containing both fuel and oxidizer, which works like a 4th of July skyrocket. *Liquid propellant*—in this type, fuel (kerosene for example) mixes with an oxidizer, such as liquid oxygen, for power.

Proximity Fuse—A fuse designed to explode a missile warhead *close* to the target instead of *against it.*

Pylon—A tower or post.

Ramjet and Pulsejet — Jet engines shaped like stovepipes, which "inhale" air and compress it, mixing it with fuel. The mixture ignites and ejects to supply thrust. Pulsejets powered the German V-1 "buzz-bombs."

Rocket—A simple combustion engine carrying its own supply of oxygen, which enables it to fly in airless upper atmosphere.

Shaped Charges—A missile warhead built to explode within a small area for greater penetration.

Sonic — Speed of sound; *subsonic:* speed less than sound; *supersonic:* faster than sound; *hypersonic:* speeds five times, or more, greater than sound.

Sounding Rockets — Rocket-powered missiles that carry instruments to high altitudes for measuring atmospheric data, such as cosmic radiation, ultra-violet intensity, temperatures, etc.

Static Testing—Ground testing under conditions similar to actual flight.

Sustainer—The engine that lifts a missile or rocket off the ground.

Telemetering—The use of radio waves to record and transmit information from a vehicle to the ground.

Turbojet—A jet engine which compresses its own air with a turbine.

Warhead—The explosive charge in the nose of a missile.

Zero - length Launcher — A mechanism, usually of rails or tubes, which instantly launches an aircraft-type, winged missile.

Abbreviations

AAM — Air-to-air missile
ATM — Anti-tank missile
ASM — Air-to-surface missile
SAM — Surface-to-air missile
SSM — Surface-to-surface missile
USM — Underwater-to-surface missile
UUM — Underwater-to-underwater missile
SRBM — Short-range ballistic missile
MRBM — Medium-range ballistic missile
IRBM — Intermediate-range ballistic missile
ICBM — Intercontinental ballistic missile
SP (R) — Solid propellant (rocket)
LP (R) — Liquid propellant (rocket)
RJ — Ramjet
PJ — Pulsejet
TJ — Turbojet